The Sweet Flypaper of Life

The
Sweet
Flypaper
of
Life

ROY DeCARAVA and LANGSTON HUGHES

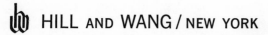 HILL AND WANG / NEW YORK

Copyright, ©, 1955, by Roy DeCarava and Langston Hughes
Library of Congress Catalog Card Number: 67-26855

First Hill and Wang Edition November 1967

Manufactured in the United States of America

1234567890

The Sweet Flypaper of Life

The Sweet Tyranny of Love

W hen the bicycle of the Lord bearing His messenger with a telegram for Sister Mary Bradley saying "Come home" arrived at 113 West 134th Street, New York City, Sister Bradley said, "Boy, take that wire right on back to St. Peter because I am not prepared to go. I might be a little sick, but as yet I ain't no ways tired." And she would not even sign for the message—since she had read it first, while claiming she could not find her glasses to sign the slip.

"For one thing," said Sister Mary, "I want to stay here and see what this integration the Supreme Court has done decreed is going to be like."

Since integration has been, ages without end, a permanently established custom in heaven, the messenger boy replied that her curiosity could be satisfied quite easily above. But Sister Mary said she wanted to find out how integration was going to work on *earth* first, particularly in South Carolina which she was planning to visit once more before she died. So the messenger boy put his wire back in his pocket and departed.

"Come home!" said Sister Mary. "I got plenty time to come home when I get to be eighty, ninety, or a hundred and one. Of course, when I wake up some morning and find my own self dead, then I'll come home. But right now, you understand me, Lord, I'm so tangled up in living, I ain't got time to die. I got to look after Ronnie Belle:

And that baby that's sleeping in yonder which is my tenth grandchild:

And I sure got to look after Louetta, who is just starting to school:

And then there's Rodney. Now, you take Rodney:

That Rodney! The street's done got Rodney! How his father and his mother can wash their hands of Rodney, I do not know, when he is the spitting image of them both. But they done put him out, so's they can keep on good-timing themselves, I reckon:

So I told him, "Come here and live with your grandma." And he come.

Now, Lord, I don't know——why did I want to take Rodney? But since I did, do you reckon my prayers will reach down in all them king-kong basements, and sing with the juke boxes, and walk in the midnight streets with Rodney? Do you reckon, Lord? Because there's something in that boy. You know and I know there's something in Rodney. If he got lost in his youthhood, it just might not be his fault, Lord. I were wild myself when I were young——and to tell the truth, ever so once in a while, I still feels the urge. But sometimes, I wonder why the only time that boy moves fast is when he's dancing. When there's music playing, girls have to just keep looking to see where he's at, he dances so fast. *Where's he at? Where's he at?*

But when he's talking, or listening, or lounging, he just looks sleepy—drinking beer down in the basement with them boys:

Now, you take that Joe, older than Rodney, thinks he's wiser—ties a big rope of words all around Rodney, ties a rope of dreams with Cadillac headlights, and bebop horns, and girls saying, "Gimmie a ride." Rodney ain't got no car. But he's got a girl, nice girl, too—at least, she's got him. She comes down there in the super's basement when she's ready to go to a party all dressed up looking for Rodney:

And Rodney has to come upstairs here to me to borrow subway fare to take her. He never moves fast—not even to reach out his hand for a dollar—except when he's dancing. And crazy about music. Can tell you every horn that ever blowed on every juke-box record in the neighborhood:

Young folks nowadays, I don't understand them. They gets their hair all done up:

just to go and set:

and listen to a juke box . . .

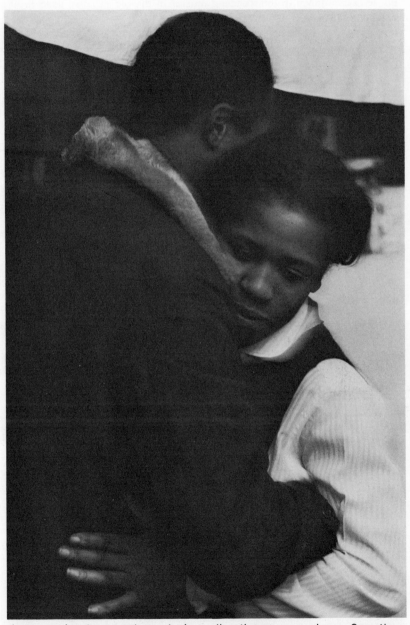

in a candy store, restaurant, bar, discotheque——anywhere. Sometimes
maybe they dance.

15

But who can dance to this bopping music? In the old days we used to like blues. And I still do:

But now the kids don't lean on the piano no more unless the piano is playing off-time. When I was young they used to play "hot" but now they play "cool." But they get just as excited as I did:

Leastwise, that's what Rodney tells me. And cars:

All the young ones nowadays is just crazy about cars:

And no wonder, because the streets is just full of cars:

In Harlem lots of roomers have got cars bigger than the room they live in. But ain't nobody in our family got a car. I wonder how come? But my oldest daughter, Mae, Chick's mother:

says they're gonna get a car. And Chickasaw, which is my most up-and-coming grandchild, declares soon as he gets married, he's gonna get one, too, so he won't have to ride the bus to work:

He always goes to work dressed up. Chick's as different from Rodney as day from night. Could dress his self when he was three years old. Gets up early in time to take the bus all the way downtown to work, don't like subways. But Rodney don't hardly get to work at all no kind of way, says daylight hurts his eyes. Never will be integrated with neither white nor colored, nor work, just won't. Now, you take Chick's girl:

Well, where she lives they got an elevator. Pretty streets, clean, it's on the hill.

How come one grandchild can get a girl from a nice family like that and another one can't? One can grow up bright——all reet, all right, as the kids say? How come two boys is so different that-a-way? Lord, help me just a little bit with that Rodney. He was always the first to turn on the hydrant in the street in the summer . . .

other boys see the water and want to get in it.

Little girls looking, egg them on:

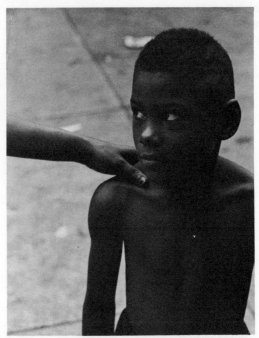

And the boys just love it.

Then the cops come—and they have to grab their clothes quick.

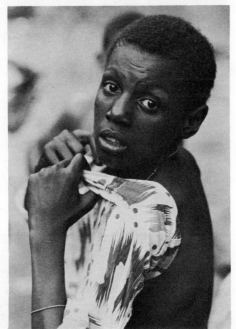

And Rodney is always the one who got caught! Too slow! Never did move fast. Never did like games like ball where you have to run:

Rather just set down in the park in the sun:

Had a baby by Sugarlee before he were even seventeen:

And he did not pay that baby no mind——did not even walk it, like other young fathers do:

Rodney's child growed up like that little boy down the street, sad.

He don't never smile.

I think it's so nice-like seeing a child talking to its father . . .

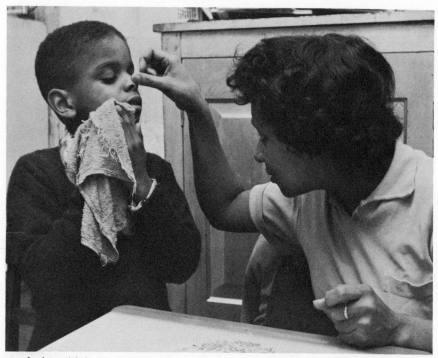

or playing with its mother.

But some children, maybe they don't have nobody:

After Rodney got in trouble with Sugarlee, that were when his father put him out, and he come to live with me—his favorite grandma. And I done climbed up and down a million subway steps:

I done rid a million subway cars, and went back and forth to work a million days for that Rodney—because he be's my favorite grandboy. Why? I don't know why. Now, you take the subway:

It's lonesome at night. But at the rush hour——well, all it took was the Supreme Court to decide on mixed schools, but the rush hour in the subway mixes everybody——white, black, Gentile, and Jew——closer than you ever are to your relatives. Now me, I always done day's work ever since I come to New York, with no extra pay for riding in the subway, which is the hardest work of all.

Sometimes when a woman comes home in the twilight evening, she's so tired she has to set down at the top of the steps to wait for the crosstown bus. Sometimes a woman goes to work all dressed up, carrying her work clothes in a bundle.

And sometimes they comes home dressed up, too.

But some be's too tired to change to come home, so they makes the trip in what they work in.

But me, I always tried to change my clothes before I come home, so's my grandchildren would see me looking fresh. I got some fine grandchildren, like my son Fred's three that lives up by the Harlem River.

Or like my daughter Ellen's daughter whose name is Ellen, too.

Oh, there is some good stock in my family. Like Ellen's mother who really takes care of her house.

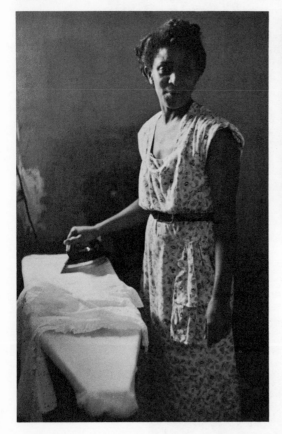

And my middle boy is well married, to a girl who is a real pretty typewriter.

And my middle daughter ain't been divorced but once and she laughs about that——so I reckon it didn't hurt her none.

Of course, I don't see how she could have liked her mother-in-law:

That old lady never thought my daughter was good enough for her son. And I never thought her son was a thing. I'm proud of me and mine, children, relatives and all! I got some fine people in my family, just like we got some fine people in our race.

We got music-making people:

and picture-painting people:

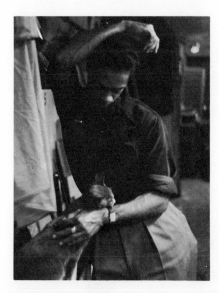

and theater-acting people,

and subway-building people:

And that sign painter that works right down in our basement:

And then we got Rodney——and he's my boy:

They say in the neighborhood sometimes Rodney can say things that makes everybody set up and take notice——even if he don't wake up till night. I used to be a kind of sleepyhead myself, so I understands him. And I think my friend, the lady that lives downstairs, she understands:

But my friends across the hall, they don't understand Rodney——nor why I worries my soul-case out about him, Sister Jenkins:

and her husband. But, of course, they never had no children, nor grandchildren neither——which is why maybe they can keep their house so clean:

Me, I always been all tangled up in life—which ain't always so sanitary as we might like it to be. Right now, whilst I'm kinder ailing and not working, I'm living with my youngest daughter, Melinda:

and her husband, Jerry.
Now you take Jerry:

And little Jerry which is his spitting image:

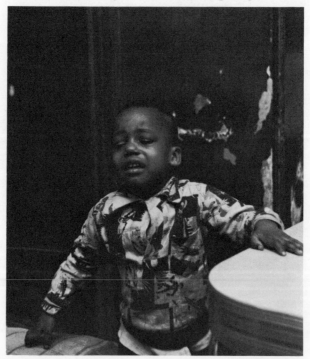

This world is like a crossword puzzle in the *Daily News*——some folks make
the puzzles, others try to solve them. But Jerry don't worry about no puzzles
a-tall. Worriation ain't no part of his nature. They been married four years
and got five children. Two is twins:

And they has a party every Saturday night:

usually not no big party:

Just neighbors and home folks.

But they balls back and stomps down:

47

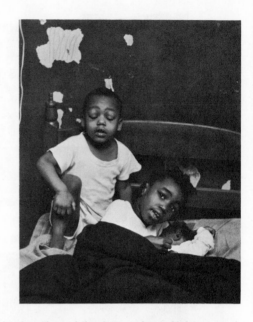

The babies is all put to bed——but they ain't always sleep. Neither am I. And sometimes when the singing starts——

I gets myself up at one-two A.M. and they say, "Mama, sing a blues." And I sings an old one I remembers:

> My blues ain't pretty.
> My blues don't satisfy—
> But they can roll like thunder
> In a rocky sky.

Sometimes when I'm singing, I remembers my youth-hood myself when I were in love with Melinda's daddy, just like she is in love with Jerry.

Sometimes when the guests get ready to go, Jerry puts on his cap and kisses his wife good-by, just like he were going somewhere, too.

He usually do mean to run out to the bar to grab himself a last-minute swig before it closes. But usually about that time one of the babies wakes up, Jerry goes and gets it:

And brings it in the kitchen:

And laughs and loves that child to sleep:

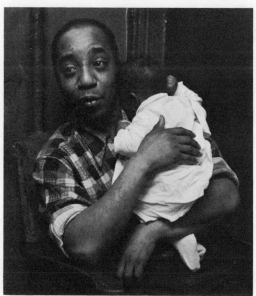

And next thing you know, both of them's done dozed off:

And that is their Saturday night.

Now you take that Jerry. There's no man living don't have some faults. Jerry's got his. But can't nobody say when he's home he ain't a family man. Crazy about his children—and his children are crazy about him:

Come running to meet him at the door:

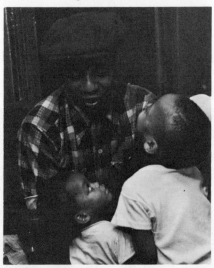

And that baby had ruther set on his lap than nurse its mama. Never saw a baby so crazy about its daddy:

But, of course, it's Melinda's got to be worried with them all day:

And sometimes, old as I is, they tries even my impatience:

And that baby is spoilt—but never cries, except when it's not setting on a lap.

Now, take little Jerry:

Well, that boy is just gun-crazy:

Says he wants a gun that shoots both ways at once:

With all them children, there's no peace until after supper:

And even then there ain't much till the bigger ones get tired:

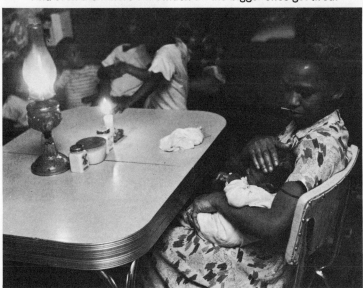

And Ronnie Belle's hair gets braided:

And everybody gets to bed, and the dishes are washed:

Maybe then Melinda gets a chance to set down and read her paper——if Jerry ain't home:

One of Jerry's faults is, he don't come home every night. Melinda got the idea she can change him. But I tells Melinda, reforming some folks is like trying to boil a pig in a coffeepot——the possibilities just ain't there——and to leave well enough alone. Long as Jerry brings his wages home, he don't always have to bring his self. And when he does come home——well, I do believe Melinda is getting ready to populate the colored race again.

Every so often, ever so once in a while, somedays a women gets a chance to set in her window for a minute and look out:

New York is not like back down South with not much happening outside. In Harlem something is happening all the time, people are going every which-a-way:

No matter which way you look, up or down, somebody is always headed somewhere, something is happening:

For some it is "Hello, so glad to see you!"

And for others . . . it's "Good-by!"

For some it's "So long! Dig you later."

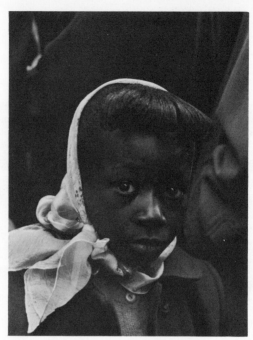

Some are out looking at parades:

Some have been where they are going.

And some can't seem to make up their minds which way to go:

And some ain't going no place at all:

But it's nice to see young folks all dressed up going somewhere——maybe to a party:

But it's sad if you ain't invited:

It's too bad there's no front porches in Harlem:

Almost nothing except stoops to set on . . .

or steps . . .   or doorways to lean in:

And in the summertime, maybe a vacant lot:

But almost everywhere where there's something to set on or lean on, somebody is setting or leaning. In what few parks there is, some just set on a park bench . . .

and hold their hands:

Yet there is so much to see in Harlem!

Tenements torn down and project houses building:

Winter coal shoveled in:

Summer ice coming:

Some folks selling, other folks buying:

Somebody always passing:

Coming and going:

Picket lines picketing:

And at night the street meetings on the corner—

talking about "Buy black":

"Africa for the Africans":

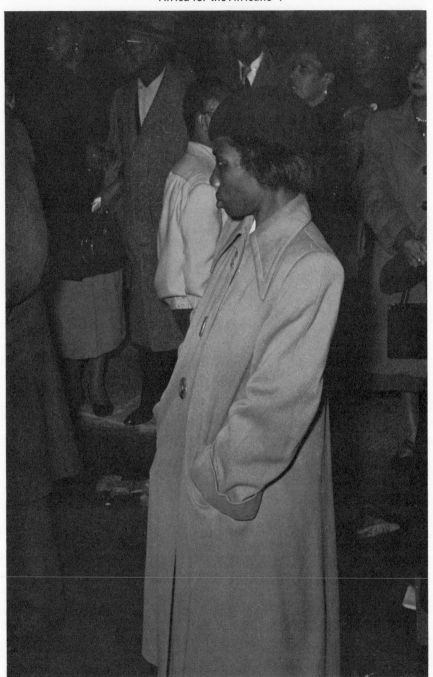

And ''Ethiopia shall stretch forth her hand'':

And some joker in the crowd always says, ''And draw back a nub!''

Yes, you can sit in your window anywhere in Harlem
and see plenty. Of course, some windows is better to
set in than others mainly because it's better inside,

not that you can necessarily see
any more. But back windows ain't
much good for looking out. I never
did like looking backwards no
how. I always did believe in looking out front—looking ahead—
which is why I's worried about
Rodney:

What do you reckon's out there in them streets for that boy?

He's my grandchild, but he seems more like my son which is why I worry so much about Rodney. Sugarlee don't worry her mind with him, and he's the father of her child. Caroline says she loves him. But she has to run and chase to find him, and he laughs:

And when she does get a hold of him, she's glad:

Rodney says he loves Ada, which is the only gal he'll ever take out anywhere much. And she is sweet.

She works, and she works hard, and sometimes when that girl gets uptown Ada's so tired she goes to sleep . . .

setting around waiting for Rodney to take her on home out of that basement where he hangs out with them beer-boys.

Ada is a decent girl. But I think maybe Rodney'd do better to marry Mazie who is somewhat like Jerry who don't give a parlor damn about paying Con Edison. Mazie works just enough to get along · · ·

which is *enough* for some people. And when Rodney takes her out, he never has to come and borrow a dollar from me. I asked him once why. Rodney said, "Maizie never hails no taxi. That girl can walk faster than me."

Mazie is already kinder beat up by life which is like I were—so she knows what it's all about. My first husband down in Carolina, which was Rodney's grandpa:

as the Irish say, *God rest his soul*—he were cut up by life, too. But it never got him down. I never knowed him to go to sleep neither, like Ada do, when loving was around. Well, anyhow, I would not choose no girl for Rodney, as I would not want no one to choose a man for me. But our janitor: his wife is dead. Do you reckon I'm too old to get married again? When I were sick he come upstairs to see me, and he said, "Miss Mary, I hear tell you's down —but with no intentions of going out."

I said, "You're right! I done got my feet caught in the sweet flypaper of life——and I'll be dogged if I want to get loose."

He said, "It is sweet, ain't it?" And ever since that time, that man's been looking at me, sort of——well, you know:

And he's crazy about children. Ronnie Belle's always playing games with that man:

And she's always peeping around the door when he comes upstairs to see me:

To tell the truth, I kinder like him myself:

As for me, well, if I do say so, I'm as good as new—back on my feet again and still kicking—with no intentions of signing no messages from St. Peter writing me to "come home." When I get through with my pots and pans . . .

ever so once in a while, I put on my best clothes.

Here I am.